THE BIG-LITTLE DINOSAUR

Story by DARLENE GEIS

Pictures by BOB JONES

Giant Wonder Books®
PRICE STERN SLOAN
Los Angeles.

Cast of Prehistoric Animals

The word dinosaur means "terrible lizard." The dinosaurs were huge animals who lived on earth more than one hundred *million* years ago. You will meet three dinosaurs and one other prehistoric animal in this story.

BRONTOSAURUS (bron-tuh-SOR-us) means "Thunder Lizard." He was called that because the ground shook when he walked. Brontosaurus was a plant-eating dinosaur. He was sixty to seventy feet long and weighed about 80,000 pounds, which is more than the weight of *seven* big elephants put together!

ALLOSAURUS (al-uh-SOR-us) was a meat-eating dinosaur, the mightiest hunter of his time. He was about thirty-five feet long.

PTERODACTYL (ter-uh-DAK-til) or "Wing-Finger," was not a bird, although he was able to fly. Birds have feathers and this animal had none. He was really a flying reptile, and his wings were made of skin stretched from one finger to his legs. He was a meat-eating reptile.

STEGOSAURUS (steg-uh-SOR-us) means "Armored Lizard." He was a plant-eating dinosaur, but because of his thick armor-like hide and huge tail, he could protect himself against his meat-eating enemies. He was fifteen to twenty feet in length. He had a very small head, with a brain the size of a walnut.

Danny was a big little dinosaur. He was big because his kind of dinosaur was TREMENDOUS. And he was little because he was still quite young.

Danny lived in a swampy marshland during the days when the world was new. Giant ferns and mosses grew everywhere. Some of them were as tall as trees and they grew as thick and green as a jungle down to the water's edge. Even the water had green plants growing in it.

The world was very strange in those olden days. Wonderful and strange creatures lived on it. But it was a lonely place for little Danny, for ever since he had hatched out of his egg he didn't know to which family he belonged.

"Some day I'll find out," he thought. But in the meantime, Danny ate and ate and ate. He was always nibbling on green ferns or moss.

One day, a large bat-winged creature flapped down out of the sky. It folded its leathery wings and looked at Danny.

"What's your name?" Danny asked.

"Pterodactyl, the Wing-Finger," the big flying creature answered.

"Hello, Pterodactyl," said Danny, glad for the company. "May I go along with you?"

"You may if you can," the Pterodactyl said with a sly grin. "But I do something you can't. I fly." And with that the Pterodactyl stretched his big wings and flapped off.

"I certainly don't belong with the Pterodactyls," sighed Danny, and he ate some more plants.

Suddenly Danny heard a strange rattle and clatter nearby. "*Now* what?" he wondered. And then he saw an odd sight. Out of the undergrowth marched a dinosaur in armor! Curving up from its neck, over its high back and down its long tail, were two rows of sharp bony plates that rattled when the animal walked. And at the tip of that remarkable tail were four strong sharp spikes.

"Ouch!" thought Danny. "I wouldn't like to bump into *him*!" But any company is better than none at all, so Danny called out, "Wh-who are *you*?"

The armored dinosaur turned his tiny head. "I'm
Stegosaurus, the Armored Lizard," he answered
proudly, and Stegosaurus rattled his bony plates.
"I'm going to eat some plants down near the water."

"I eat plants, too," said Danny. "May I come
along?" Stegosaurus nodded his little head yes and
marched on. Danny followed happily.

Stegosaurus and Danny were feasting peacefully on tender green plants, when suddenly, the earth beneath their feet shook. There was a sound like the rumbling of thunder. What could it be? Danny was alarmed but Stegosaurus went right on chewing.

"It's Brontosaurus, the Thunder Lizard," he explained with his mouth full of leaves. "He's so heavy it sounds like thunder when he walks."

Danny peeked through the ferns. There he saw
not one, but two enormous creatures plodding down
to the water's edge. Their legs were as big around
as tree trunks. Their long necks stretched up toward
the sky. Their even longer tails dragged heavily
behind them. THUMP! THUMP! THUMP! With
each step they took, the ground shook and rumbled
under their great weight.

"How frightening!" thought Danny. But the huge dinosaurs were minding their own business. They kept moving slowly toward the water, stopping once in a while to snap off a green leaf. Their heads turned this way and that as they chewed, and their look was gentle.

"Why, even though they're so big," thought the little dinosaur, "they are not fierce at all." In fact, Danny thought that they were the most beautiful creatures he had ever seen. They were moving out into the deep water, and the little dinosaur looked after them sadly.

"How I would like to do that!" said Danny. But Danny was afraid he was too small, and he didn't know if he could go out into the water. So he sighed and went on munching leaves.

All at once, there was a snorting and crashing in the underbrush. It sounded terrible. "Goodness! What's that?" Danny asked. But Stegosaurus was shifting his huge armored body around so that he stood between Danny and the bushes.

"Into the water, quick! It's Allosaurus, the giant meat-eater," he declared. "And *you're* his meat!"

Danny asked no more questions. He moved into the water as fast as he could. The giant Allosaurus came leaping out of the underbrush with his huge jaws snapping.

But Stegosaurus kept him from the water's edge. *Whack! Whack!* A few mighty slaps with that spiked tail, and Allosaurus went limping back into the jungle to tend his wounds.

"Thank you, Stegosaurus!" Danny called to his friend from the water. But Stegosaurus was rattling his armor proudly and didn't hear.

"I'm alone again," thought Danny sadly. And he bent his head to nibble on one of the water plants.

Just then two big dinosaurs came up beside him.
"Hello, little Brontosaurus," they said gently.

"So *that's* what I am!" Danny exclaimed. "I'm a
Brontosaurus!" And he moved over closer to the
two huge dinosaurs.

The three dinosaurs stood there like three islands in the quiet water — two large islands and one small one — all eating plants. How nice not to be alone any more! The strange new world seemed safe and happy now. Danny had found his family.